Folens
Words at Work ✓

3

Word-level and Sentence-level Work for Excellence in Spelling and Grammar

JO PHENIX

Hello! I am Buzzy Bee.
Welcome to
Words at Work ✓,
a book of activities and games
to help you to become a
better reader and writer.

First published in the United Kingdom in 1999 by

Folens Publishers
Albert House
Apex Business Centre
Boscombe Road
Dunstable
Bedfordshire
LU5 4RL

Jo Phenix hereby asserts her moral right to be identified as the author of this work in accordance with the Copyright, Designs and Patents Act 1988. Additional material by Mary Green.

Editor: Jennifer Steele   Layout artist: James Brown
Illustrations: Sue Woollatt (Graham-Cameron Illustration)
          Liz Sawyer (Simon Girling & Associates)
          Mike Lacey (Simon Girling & Associates)
          Sarah Hedley (Graham-Cameron Illustration)
Cover artist: Carl H. Wiens   Cover design: Martin Cross
Page design: Turners Creative

British Library Cataloguing in Publication Data.
A catalogue record for this book is available from the British Library.
Printed in Hong Kong through World Print.

ISBN 1 86202 620-3
UK edition © Folens 1999.

© 1997 developed by Harcourt Brace & Company Canada, Ltd.
All rights reserved. Published by special arrangement with Harcourt Brace & Company Canada, Ltd.

Words at Work ✔

Contents

What Am I?

In many words, two **consonants** make just one sound. For example, in the word *phase*, the letters **ph** make the **f** sound.

A Solve these riddles to fill in the **ph** words:

Copy and Complete
1. pharaoh

1. In ancient times, I was the ruler of Egypt.
I was buried in a pyramid.
Who am I?

2. I ring to attract attention.
Use me to talk to your friends far away.
What am I?

3. I am a large grey animal with four knees.
My trunk is my personal shower.
What am I?

4. I can balance a ball on my nose.
I can leap high out of the water.
What am I?

5. I am awarded to winners.
I may be a silver cup or statue.
What am I?

6. I can be put into a picture frame.
I am taken by a camera.
What am I?

7. I am a place where you can buy medicine.
I am another name for a chemist's shop.
What am I?

8. I am a branch of science.
My scientists study heat, light and sound.
What am I?

B Can you write any names with a **ph** sounding like **f**? For example: Philippa.

Remember ph in words sound like **f**.

Listen Softly

Listen to the **c** sound in these words:

● *cat   curtain   cotton.*

It is called **hard c** and sounds like **k**.

Listen to the **c** sound in these words:

● *cinder   ace   city.*

It is called **soft c** and sounds like **s**.

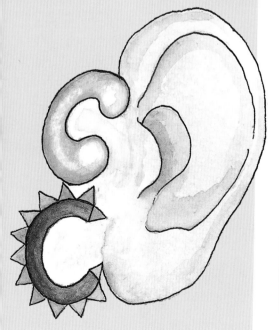

This rhyme will help you to remember this spelling pattern: i, y and e soften c.

A   Draw a chart like this:

Soft c words		
ce	ci	cy

● Read the list of words below carefully. Choose the **soft c** words from the list and write them in the correct place on your chart.

cygnet	candle	cedar	cap
coin	cabbage	cinema	prince
city	placid	cucumber	space
cement	cell	peace	comic
cup	certain	cylinder	cactus
come	cinder	ace	

B   Now write two sentences, one using **soft c** words and one using **hard c** words. Your sentences can be silly or serious. For example: The placid cygnet went to the cinema.

Remember When you hear a *soft c* it should be followed by **i**, **y** or **e**.

Vowel Riddles

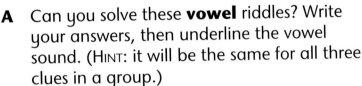

A Can you solve these **vowel** riddles? Write your answers, then underline the vowel sound. (HINT: it will be the same for all three clues in a group.)

B Now add one more word to each group and write a clue for it.

What do people make that you can't see?

Noise.

Copy and Complete

1. a. Heat water to make me happen.   b<u>oi</u>l
   b. I am money made out of metal.   c<u>oi</u>n
   c. I disturb people and I can be very loud.   n<u>oi</u>se

1. a. Heat water to make me happen.
   b. I am money made out of metal.
   c. I disturb people and I can be very loud.

2. a. A child may play with me.
   b. I am the opposite of a girl.
   c. I am a happy feeling.

3. a. You can get milk from me.
   b. I appear on an unhappy face.
   c. I am a question word.

4. a. I describe someone who is a king or queen.
   b. Open me up and you may find a pearl.
   c. I am a long journey.

5. a. You can use me to tie back your hair.
   b. I am white and cold and I fall in winter.
   c. I am a large, black bird.

Remember Learning words together that have the same vowel sounds will help you to remember them.

6

G for George

Listen to the **g** sound in these words:

● *go   gate   grab.*

It is called **hard g**.

Listen to the **g** sound in these words:

● *George   giant   gym.*

It is called **soft g** and sounds like **j**.

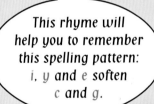

This rhyme will help you to remember this spelling pattern: i, y and e soften c and g.

A   Draw a chart like this:

Soft g words		
ge	gi	gy

● Read the list of words below carefully. Choose the **soft g** words from the list and write them in the correct place on your chart.

ginger	orange	gobble	Egypt	germ
Gill	Graham	magic	game	smudge
general	goose	gentle	giraffe	gypsy
gyroscope	gin	cage	gem	energy
gymkhana	garden	garage	goat	gymnasium

B   One word has both a **soft** and a **hard g**. Which is it?

C   These words do not fit into this spelling pattern:

get	tiger	giggle

● Can you think of one more word that does not fit the spelling pattern? Look out for other exceptions as you read and write, and note them in your book.

D   Now write two sentences, one using **soft g** words and one using **hard g** words. Your sentences can be silly or serious. For example: The gentle giant played with the giraffe in the gym.

Remember When you hear a *soft g* it should usually be followed by **i**, **y** or **e**.

Piece It Together

A Use this spelling rhyme to help you to spell the answers to these riddles: '**i** before **e**, when it sounds like **ee**, except after **c**.' REMEMBER: all your answers must contain either the **ie** or **ei** spelling.

1. I am the daughter of your brother.

2. Because I steal things, I am often called this.

3. To serve me, cut me into several of these.

4. I protect my knight in battle.

5. I often make people cry out like this.

6. You can tie your boat to me.

7. Ride me through the snow.

8. I live next door to you.

9. Your blood flows through me.

10. Use me to lead your horse.

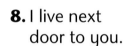

11. Use me to balance a scale.

12. These provide grass for cows.

Remember When it sounds like **ee**, put the **i** before **e**, except after **c**.

L Scramble

A Read the clues to help you to unscramble these words containing **l**. (HINT: the answers in each group are rhyming words.)

● Now add your own word to each group, following the same pattern.

Copy and Complete
1. a. I describe men and boys.   *lema* = male

1. a. I describe men and boys. *lema*
   b. You can get bargains at the shops when I am there. *asle*
   c. You can play me with eight musical notes. *ecasl*

2. a. I am the letters that are delivered to your home. *laim*
   b. You strike me with a hammer. *lnia*
   c. I fall as ice from the sky. *ahil*

3. a. I am shaped like a snake, but I live in the water. *ele*
   b. I am part of your foot. *lehe*
   c. A bicycle has two of me. *wlehe*

4. a. You eat me three times a day. *leam*
   b. I am the opposite of fake. *earl*
   c. I can balance a ball on my nose and swim at the same time. *esla*

5. a. I am the cry of a wolf. *owhl*
   b. I am another word for frown. *wcsol*
   c. I am thought to be a wise bird. *lwo*

Remember Learning words with the same letter pattern will help to improve your spelling.

Future Riddles

Read the following sentence:

● A nature adventure with a creature of the future.

Which words end with the sound 'cher'?
Notice that this sound is spelled **ture**.

A Solve these riddles with words ending in **ture**:

1. I hang on the wall. I may show a person or a scene. What am I?

2. I am usually green and lush. I may be a home for cows. What am I?

3. I have not yet happened. I am the opposite of the past. What am I?

4. I deal with the environment. I involve everything that lives. What am I?

5. Explorers seek me out. I am a type of story. What am I?

6. I am an animal. I may be from outer space. What am I?

7. People fill their rooms with me. You can sit on me or eat from me. What am I?

8. I am a smaller version of something. I may be a type of golf. What am I?

9. I am the opposite of release. I mean to take prisoner. What am I?

10. I am a work of art. A sculptor makes me. What am I?

CREATURE OF THE FUTURE

NATURE PARK
SCULPTURE ADVENTURE

Remember The ending **ture** sounds like 'cher'.

Rough Weather

Some words have the same letter pattern but different sounds:

- *th**ough***
- *br**ough**t.*

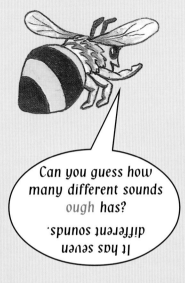

Can you guess how many different sounds *ough* has?

It has seven different sounds.

A   Choose the **ough** words from the list below and complete the sentences:

measure	bought	light	foot
coughs	boot	bright	doughnut
treasure	rough	leisure	through
plough	tight	thorough	

1. Leroy took one bite of the _____ and threw it away.
2. _____ *the Looking Glass* follows *Alice in Wonderland.*
3. _____ and colds are always troublesome.
4. The farmer mended his old _____ ready to use in the fields.
5. The twins unwittingly _____ each other the same birthday present.
6. "_____ weather!" said the mole as his umbrella blew inside out.
7. He was always _____ and the room was cleaned to perfection.

B   Can you find any other words in the list above that have the same letter pattern, but sound different?

Remember Some words have the same letter pattern but different sounds.

A Trip to the Zoo

Read the following:

- We're *booking* a trip to the *zoo*.

Booking sounds like *putting*; *zoo* sounds like *you*.

The **oo** sound is common in English, but not all **oo** words sound the same:

- Ahh! There's *blood* on the *floor*!

Blood sounds like *mud*; *floor* sounds like *paw*.

A Make two columns. Write the headwords **put** and **you**. Sort each word in the list below into the group that sounds the same as the headword.

foot	moon	soon	cook
wood	look	gloom	good
mood	fool	book	hood
boot	troop	roof	cool
rook	swoop	took	stood

B Make two more columns and write the headwords **mud** and **paw**. Do the same as you did in exercise **A**.

floor	blood	poor	flooring
moor	flood	bloodhound	
door	Exmoor	bloodsucker	
poorly	doorstep	floodlight	

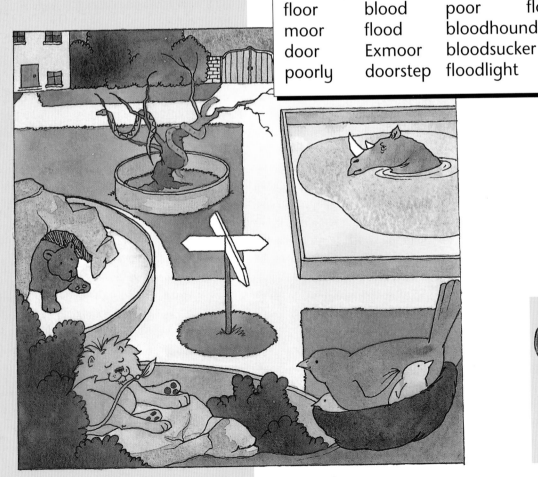

Remember oo has four different sounds.

No Stress!

Some words have **vowels** which we do **not stress** when we say them:

● Sue will interview the astr**o**naut.

The vowel **o** is not stressed in *astronaut*. It makes the same light sound as **er** in *bak**er***.

What sound is not stressed in *interview*?

A Write out these words and underline the vowel that is not stressed:

company	portable	poisonous
interest	description	carpet
sector	freedom	extra
capable	error	kingdom
descent	compass	motor

● Split the words into syllables to help you to remember how to spell them.

B Think of six questions that Sue could ask the astronaut about her trip to the moon. Use the words shown in the picture.

When is a vowel happy?

When it's not stressed!

Remember Some words have *vowels* which we do *not stress* when we say them.

Pirate's Treasure

A **syllable** is a group of letters that forms part or all of a word. Each syllable is one beat in a word when you say it out loud.

Remember that every syllable has a vowel!

A Think of objects that a pirate might want as treasure. You can use the objects in the chest below to help you. Help Captain Crook to make a list of his treasure by sorting the items into lists of one, two or three syllables. Say the words to yourself to help you to count the syllables.

Copy and Complete

one syllable	two syllables	three syllables
ring	goblet	amethyst

Remember Splitting words into *syllables* can help you to spell.

Prefix Search

A **prefix** is a group of letters added to the beginning of a word to change its meaning. The same prefix can often be used with many different words. When you add a prefix to a word, the spelling of the word stays the same.

A The prefix **re** means 'again' as in *redo*. It can also mean 'back' as in the word *return*. Find the words in the wordsearch that can be used with the prefix **re.** Make a list of your new words – for example, adding **re** to *place* makes *replace*. If you need to circle the words as you find them, carefully copy the wordsearch first.

● Words can go across and down.

p	l	a	c	e	c	r	e	a	t	e	a	s	t
f	m	m	y	s	o	a	l	y	t	d	t	p	r
i	a	z	c	t	p	h	e	a	t	i	h	e	a
l	k	v	l	y	y	a	c	u	t	t	i	l	c
l	e	t	e	l	l	s	t	r	a	i	n	l	e
e	i	u	s	e	f	a	s	t	e	n	k	d	e
d	o	r	u	s	i	g	n	t	r	e	a	t	o
u	a	n	y	e	r	e	c	o	r	d	a	b	p
c	v	t	r	n	u	p	p	a	e	s	r	d	e
a	w	i	n	d	s	y	a	a	s	f	g	h	n
t	b	u	i	l	d	i	y	s	h	a	p	e	z
e	x	a	m	i	n	e	b	c	v	i	e	w	z
a	e	n	t	e	r	a	y	t	a	k	e	a	a

Remember When you add a *prefix* to a word, the spelling of the word remains the same.

Prefix Quiz

A Solve the **prefix** quiz by answering the questions. Use the list of prefixes to help you.

bi	**tri**	**quad**	**centi**	**sub**	**tele**	**circum**	**trans**	**auto**
two	three	four	one hundred	under	far	around	across	self

1. If the root *ped* means 'foot', name three animals that are *quadrupeds*.
2. Name two animals that are *bipeds*.
3. Are humans *bipeds* or *quadrupeds*?
4. How many legs does a *centipede* seem to have?
5. What type of *marine* travels underwater?
6. If *tele* means 'far' and *scope* means 'to see', what would you use to see something far away?
7. What would you call a *cycle* with three wheels?
8. What geometrical shape has three sides?
9. You can speak to someone far away using one of these.
10. If you speak two languages, you are this.
11. What is the distance around a circle called?
12. What is a book that tells your life story called?
13. You do this when you carry something from one place to another.

What did the centipede say in the shoe shop?

I need a new pair of shoes, new pair of shoes, new pair of shoes ...

B Use each of the prefixes in the box above to write another word.

Remember Learn the meanings of *prefixes* to help you to remember their spellings.

Prefix Race

Study the meaning of these **prefixes**:

inter   *between*
pro   *for, forward*
suc, **sus**   *after, under.*

il
im
in   } *in, into, upon, not*
ir

A   Try to work out roughly what these words mean by looking at their prefixes:

succession	procedure	illuminate
suspect	irrigate	intercept
intertwine	suspend	projection
inclusion	impending	intensive

● Now look up the words in a dictionary and see how close you were.

B   Turn the words below into their opposite meaning by adding the correct prefix, choosing from **il**, **im**, **in** or **ir**:

regular	logical	mortal
responsible	tangible	firm
legal	mature	

C   Choose six words that you are uncertain how to spell. Split them into **syllables**, then ask a friend to check your spelling.

Remember A *prefix* can help you to work out the meaning of a word.

Find the Roots

A **root word** is a small word that forms part of a longer word, for example, **act** in *react*.

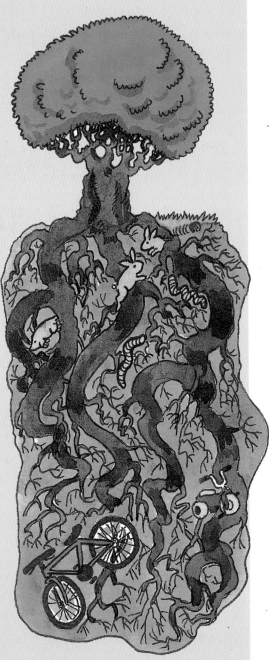

A   Solve the clues to find the hidden roots below.

  1. I describe something that can be moved.
  2. I usually carry your luggage to your hotel room.
  3. Teachers write these about their pupils' school work.
  4. I am a word for cars, trucks and vehicles used to move people and things from place to place.

●   What is the root word? Now think of a new word using this root and write a sentence using it.

B   **1.** I consist of one hundred years.
  2. I seem to have one hundred legs.
  3. I am celebrated after one hundred years.
  4. There are one hundred of me in an American dollar.

●   What is the root word? Now think of a new word using this root and write a sentence using it.

C   **1.** I have two wheels and one seat.
  2. I have three wheels and two pedals.
  3. Help the environment by doing me.

●   What is the root word? Now think of a new word using this root and write a sentence using it.

Remember A *root word* is a small word that forms part of a longer word.

Roots Plus

Roots can have **prefixes** and **suffixes** added to them to build new words: for example, *gold* becomes *golden*.

A Build as many words as you can using the roots and suffixes below (be aware of cases where you will need to drop the **silent e**). Make a list of your words.

Copy and Complete
harm + less = harmless

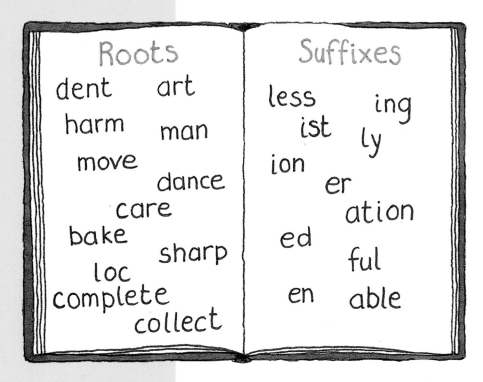

Roots
dent   art
harm   man
move
        dance
    care
bake
    sharp
    loc
complete
    collect

Suffixes
less   ing
    ist ly
ion
    er
        ation
ed
    ful
en   able

B Can you think of a word to which you can add more than one suffix at a time?

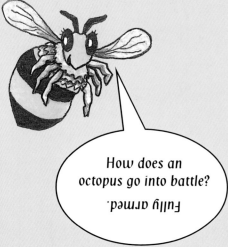

How does an octopus go into battle?

Fully armed.

Remember Practising making words using *roots* will help you to learn to spell them.

What's My Line?

A The **suffix ology** means 'the science or study of'. Copy the sentences below and fill in the missing students, matching them with their subject. (HINT: Look in the illustration for help with the subjects.)

I am Eric the Elasticman. I can escape from anything. I am an escapolog**ist**. I am an expert on escap**ology**.

musicology
ecology biology
archaeology
criminology
zoology radiology
cosmology
cryptology
ornithology
meteorology
psychology

Copy and Complete

1. I study life. I am a <u>biologist</u>. My subject is called <u>biology</u>.

1. I study life. I am a _____ . My subject is called _____ .

2. I study the environment. I am an _____ . My subject is called _____ .

3. I study ancient relics. I am an _____ . My subject is called _____ .

4. I study crime. I am a _____ . My subject is called _____ .

5. I study the weather. I am a _____ . My subject is called _____ .

6. I study radiation. I am a _____ . My subject is called _____ .

7. I study animals. I am a _____ . My subject is called _____ .

8. I study the universe. I am a _____ . My subject is called _____ .

B How many other **ology** words can you add?

C The ending **ist** often shows a person who does a kind of job, for example a typ**ist**. How many other jobs can you think of that end in **ist**?

Remember The ending **ology** can describe a type of job while the ending **ist** describes the person who does it.

Shun Collection

When you hear the sound 'shun' at the end of a word, it will most often be spelled with the **suffix tion**, as in *protection.* When you hear the sound 'ashun', it will almost always be spelled **ation.**

What kind of table has no legs?

A multiplication table.

A There are 16 words ending in **tion** or **ation** in this wordsearch. Make a list of the words that you can find. If you need to circle the words as you find them, carefully copy the wordsearch first.

● The words go across and down.

s	f	o	u	n	d	a	t	i	o	n	a	c	p	c
t	r	e	l	a	t	i	o	n	c	t	a	e	u	o
a	d	d	i	t	i	o	n	v	i	f	n	l	n	l
t	b	c	w	x	y	d	e	e	r	o	i	r	c	l
i	z	a	i	d	h	g	f	s	c	r	m	a	t	e
o	b	c	j	r	e	f	g	t	u	m	a	t	u	c
n	a	t	i	o	n	h	i	i	l	a	t	i	a	t
p	e	t	i	t	i	o	n	g	a	t	i	o	t	i
s	t	a	h	a	l	o	c	a	t	i	o	n	i	o
v	a	c	a	t	i	o	n	t	i	o	n	e	o	n
u	v	h	a	i	v	k	j	i	o	n	s	b	n	p
w	y	s	x	o	t	i	n	o	n	y	u	k	p	o
q	r	m	l	n	r	m	n	n	o	p	k	l	m	n

B There are a few 'ashun' words that do not end in the spelling **ation**. Several of them are breeds of dogs. Can you name them?

 **Remember** The ending **tion** sounds like 'shun'.

Using Your Imagination

Some **suffixes** sound the same but have different spellings:

- I made a deci**sion** to write a composi**tion** about a magi**cian**.

The suffixes **sion**, **tion** and **cian** sound like 'shun'.

A Read the following passage and write down all the words that end with the 'shun' sound under three lists:

Copy and Complete		
sion	tion	cian

There was an explosion of sound! The musicians began to play as Melchior the Mighty stepped on to the stage, producing a collection of coloured ribbons from under his hat. The tiniest children squealed with delight as the magician performed illusion after illusion. The music grew louder. The percussion boomed. The tension grew. Melchior stepped back. From thin air, a beautiful unicorn appeared. Was it real or was it an apparition? Marianne could not answer that question but, as the unicorn galloped away, her imagination took hold. She would write the best composition she had ever thought of!

B Match these clues to the correct words from the passage above.
1. They make beautiful music.
2. All together.
3. Melchior the Mighty.
4. Now you see it, now you don't.
5. The drums and cymbals.
6. The written word.

C Now write Marianne's story. Use the picture to help you.

Remember The *suffixes* **sion**, **tion** and **cian** sound the same.

Drop That Letter

When you add a **suffix** to a word ending in **e**, you must decide when to drop the **e** and when to keep it:

- If you add an ending beginning with a **vowel**, drop the **e**.
- If you add an ending beginning with a **consonant**, do not drop the **e**.

A Use these rules to build words using the **root words** and **suffixes** below. The root words are in black ink and the suffixes are in red.

Copy and Complete

wise + ly = wisely   fine + est = finest

wise able love
fine ful use give est
like safe nice fame
ly ing ed ous

For example:

- A whale is the **larg est** animal in the world.
- A giraffe's long neck is **use ful** for reaching leaves on high branches.

B Now choose four of the new words you have built and write sentences containing them.

Remember If a word ends in a *silent* **e** and you add an ending beginning with a *vowel*, drop the **e**; if you add an ending beginning with a *consonant*, keep the **e**.

A Day at the Seaside

When a word ends in **y** with a **consonant** before it, change the **y** to **ie** when you add a **suffix**:

● *dry dries dried.*

However, when the suffixes **ly** and **ing** are added, the **y** stays:

● *drying dryly.*

A There are 11 spelling mistakes in the following passage. Follow the rule to find them and write them out correctly.

Copy and Complete
1. tryed   tried

Yesterday we tryed to have a picnic! It was warm and sunny so we packed a large basket of food and went to the beach. "Bet it'll be blue skys all summer!" laughed my brother. "Let's hope so!" I replyed. We spyed the perfect spot, put down the basket and ran into the sea.

When we returned, everything was covered in insects. There were ants on the food and sandflys all over our clothes. A dog had buryed his nose in the basket. We shooed him away and a small crab popped out of the basket. It looked at me sliely and scuttled off. As the crab disappeared the weather changed. It began to rain. We got wetter and wetter and my small sister began crieing. She did not stop until we got home and her clothes had dryed.

At home, my father greeted us, "Don't worry, I've fryed some prawns for supper!" he said driely.

Remember There are rules for changing and keeping **y**.

Cheerful Charlie

When we use the word *full* alone it has a double **ll**:

- All seats are **full**!

When we use it as a **suffix** we drop one **l**:

- Cheer**ful** Charlie and Mourn**ful** Maurice.

Put full and fill together and what do you get?

Fulfil.

A Add the **ful** suffix to the words in the clown's hoop.

power   pain
use   thank
wonder   care
hate   hope
help   truth
spoon   faith

B Copy these sentence starters about the circus and complete them using **ful** words. For example: The circus was wonderful!

1. The circus was _____ .

2. Aunt Millie _____ .

3. We were given _____ .

4. No animals _____ .

5. The acrobats _____ .

6. The flying trapeze _____ .

7. _____ Charlie _____ .

8. _____ Maurice _____ .

Remember When *full* is a *suffix* you drop one **l**: ful.

Wetter and Wetter!

Read the following words:

● *wet   wetting   wetter*
● *shop   shopped.*

Note this rule: when a word ends with a single **consonant** preceded by a short **vowel**, we double the consonant before adding **ing**, **ed** or **er**.

A Copy and complete the table below correctly. Note that not all spaces will be filled. Follow the rule!

Root word	ing	ed	er
run			
hum			
pop			
shop			
swim			
stop			
flat			
blot			
trip			
split			

B Now choose three words from the table and include them in a single sentence. Try to use a different ending for each word. For example: Aaron trip**ped** as he went shop**ping** for a blott**er**.

Remember When simple words end in a *consonant*, double the last letter before adding an ending beginning with a *vowel*.

Syllable Count

Listen to the last **syllable** of each of these words:

● sick   Atlantic
  pick   dynamic.

The words end with the sound 'ik', but have different spellings – **ick** and **ic**.

How do hares get their exercise?

They do hare-robics.

A Sort these words into two groups – words of one syllable and words with more than one syllable. Make two lists of your words.

Copy and Complete	
One syllable	More than one syllable
flick	terrific

flick	sick	terrific
quick	public	electric
arithmetic	Antarctic	Atlantic
tragic	poetic	Arctic
trick	stick	plastic
slick	volcanic	panic
metric	tick	wick
pick	magic	

B What rule have you discovered about how to spell the 'ik' sound at the end of these words? Use this rule to answer the following quiz. The answers end with either **ic** or **ick**.

1. What is the world's largest ocean called?
2. If you feel ill on a ship, what might you be?
3. What word describes something that has the properties of a magnet?
4. What is a meal eaten in a park or the country called?

Remember Words of one *syllable* end in **ick** like this: *pick*.
Words of more than one syllable end in **ic** like this: *dynamic*.

Plural Party

When a word means that there is just one thing, it is a **singular** word:

● *bottle   beach   cup.*

When a word means that there is more than one thing, then it is **plural:**

● *bottle**s** beach**es** cup**s.***

What insects does a blacksmith make?

Fireflies.

A Imagine you are going on a picnic. Write ten sentences to tell the story of your day. You might write about what you took, where you went, what you did and how you felt. Use as many words on the tablecloth as you can in the plural. There are three different plural patterns (**s**, **es** and **ies**).

box   birch
peach   pony
bench   porch   fox
bottle   puppy
bus   story   plate
fly   butterfly
family   berry

Remember Check that you know the common *plural* patterns.

Find the Plurals

Some words do not follow regular plural patterns. They are **irregular plurals**.

Some plural words remain the same as the singular word.

A Look at the pictures below. Use the clues to give you the plural words. Carefully copy the number of dashes and the position of the box in each word. The letters in the boxes will give you a 'mystery plural'.

1. _ _ _ □ _

2. _ □ _ _ _

3. _ □ _ _ _

4. _ □ _ _

5. □ _ _ _ _

6. □ _ _ _ _ _ _ _ _ _

7. _ _ _ _ □ _

8. _ □ _ _

● What is the mystery plural?

B Make a list of the words that stayed the same and a list of those that changed.

C Can you think of any other irregular plurals?

What is a sea monster's favourite meal?

Fish and ships.

Remember Learn groups of *irregular plurals* to help you to remember their spellings.

Plurals by Themselves

Words that end in **f** often have unusual **plurals**.
To make the plural, you take away the **f** and add **ves**.
So, one el**f** becomes two el**ves**.

You will probably never see the plural rooves. It is better to write roofs.

A Copy these sentences, using plurals ending in **ves** to complete them.
● Beside each sentence, write the singular word.

Copy and Complete	Singular word
1. The cows and their young <u>calves</u> enjoyed the fresh spring grass.	calf

1. The cows and their young _____ enjoyed the fresh spring grass.
2. We shared the chocolate bar by cutting it into two _____ .
3. The husbands played on one team, while the _____ played on the other.
4. We set the table with _____ and forks for dinner.
5. At night, we could hear the howling of a pack of _____ in the forest.
6. We will need three _____ of bread to make the sandwiches.
7. The horse's _____ made a great clatter as we galloped over the bridge.
8. The three of us spent the night in a tent by our _____ .
9. When we saw the bull in the field, we ran for our _____ .

B Look out for the word *dwarf*, the plural of which can be written in two ways:
dwarves　　　*dwarfs*
● Look in one or two versions of the story *Snow White*. Which of these plural spellings is used?

 **Remember** To make *plurals* from words that end in **f**, you usually drop the **f** and add **ves**.

1st Prize

There are many ways in which we can make words and phrases shorter. For example, we can lose letters:

- *o'clock* means *of the clock*
- we usually write *plane* for *aeroplane.*

Sometimes we make new words from the first letters of words:

- **ra**dio **d**etection **a**nd **r**anging was the original term for *radar.*

Sometimes we combine words or drop words:

- *zoological gardens* is the long form of *zoo.*

A Give either the short or long version of these words:

phone	omnibus	permanent wave
mike	flu	motorbike	Xmas
rock 'n' roll	exam	petrol
high-technology	tel	refrigerator

B Write down the long version of these:

| BBC | vet | hi-fi | kg |
| NW | movie | fax | CD |

C Work out the meaning of these abbreviations:

1st: Gold
2nd: Silver
3rd: Bronze
Runner-up: £5

Admission: 50p
OAPs: Free

Remember We shorten words in many ways.

Turn Around

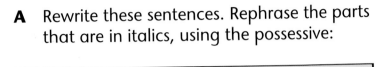

Possessives show ownership. For example, in the phrase *the rose's scent*, the **'s** shows that the scent belongs to the rose.

A Rewrite these sentences. Rephrase the parts that are in italics, using the possessive:

Copy and Complete

1. Kezban was fascinated by the *tricks of the magician.*
Kezban was fascinated by the *magician's tricks.*

---

1. Kezban was fascinated by the *tricks of the magician.*
2. The *rumbling of the thunder* scared the horses.
3. Ritu became entangled in the *tail of the kite.*
4. Alice was surprised by the *size of the rabbit hole.*
5. Captain Hook was afraid whenever he heard the *ticking of the crocodile clock.*

B With plural words ending in an **s**, you do not need to add another **s** to make the possessive. Just add the apostrophe. For example: The girls' team. Rewrite the sentences below, rephrasing the parts in italics by using the plural possessive.

1. We were awakened every morning by the *singing of the birds.*
2. We danced all evening to the *beat of the drums.*
3. The *music of the bands* made the parade exciting.
4. The *saddles of the horses* were very comfortable.

What's as big as an elephant but doesn't weigh anything?

The elephant's shadow.

Remember The apostrophe can be used to show that something belongs to something else or to a group of people.

Whose Is It?

Some **possessives** do not use an **'s** to show ownership: for example, *our* house, *your* car. These words are called **possessive pronouns.**

his
her
our
your
mine
their
ours
my
hers
its
theirs
yours

A Copy the sentences below and use the possessive pronouns on the scroll to finish them. Use each word only once.

1. Karen left _____ new coat on the bus.
2. Ralph rode _____ bike to school.
3. The dog knocked over _____ bowl.
4. Carmen found the wrapped presents, but she was not sure if they were _____ .
5. "That book is _____ ."
6. The children were disappointed because _____ picnic was cancelled.
7. "I'm going to _____ room to read a book."
8. "When is _____ next doctor's appointment?"
9. We missed _____ final game because the car broke down.
10. The twins think the new computer is _____ .
11. "Is this video game _____ ?"
12. "That fishing boat is _____ ," said the two fishermen.

How does an alien count to 30?

On its fingers.

Remember *Possessive pronouns* do not need to use an **'s** to show ownership.

33

Yours and Mine

You will remember that we use words such as *yours* and *mine* to show that something belongs to someone or something else and they are called **possessive pronouns**. For example: The King was in the counting house counting gold coins. When he had finished he announced to the Queen:

● "What's yours is mine and what's mine is my own."

Why was this unfair?

A Copy the sentences below, completing them using the correct possessive pronouns.

| mine | her | ours | its | my |

1. The Queen said the gold coins belonged to _____ .
2. "No," said the twin princes, "those gold coins are _____ ."
3. "Woof!" barked the royal spaniel. "If they're anyone's they're _____ ."
4. The Chancellor interrupted, "In _____ view, the coins belong to the treasury and the treasury must decide what to do with _____ money."

your
yours his
our
hers their
theirs

B Now write your own sentences using the possessive pronouns in the King's thought bubble.

Remember A *possessive pronoun* is used to show that something belongs to someone or something.

Dear Joanna

A All the **apostrophes** have been left out of this letter. Rewrite the letter, putting the apostrophes in the correct places.

● Make sure you add apostrophes to the **contractions** and **possessives**, and not to the **plurals** unless they are possessive.

Dear Joanna,

Im writing from my aunts farm, where my family and I are spending our holiday. Were having a great time. The birds singing wakes us up early every morning.

There are horses, chickens, cows and pigs on the farm. The horses stable is a great place to play. Its our job to collect eggs, and we have to climb up the barns ladder to the loft. The cockerel also has its perch up there. A farmers work is never done, it seems!

The sheep and cows have many babies. Weve been to see them every day. All the cows calves are wobbly on their legs, but the lambs are already running around the fields. The lambs are Theos favourites, but he also likes grooming the horses tails. He has adopted one of the ponies, and spends time every day cleaning out his ponys stable.

The children from the next farm come over every day. Well be going over to their place tomorrow with our football.

How are your baby kittens? Is the cats basket getting a bit crowded? Theyll soon be as big as our cats litter, even though ours are two weeks older. We havent even found names for them all, but it shouldnt take us much longer. We found a book of names in Auntys bookcase.

Ill have to close now. Were all going to Grandads place. Hes promised to show us his emus! There arent many of those around here!

Ill see you soon.

Love from Flora

Remember Make sure you put *apostrophes* in the correct places.

Cyclone Cyril

We often use the **apostrophe** incorrectly when we write:
● The hurricane ran *it's* course.

We have really written:
● The hurricane ran *it is* course.

It's with an apostrophe is a **contraction** of *it is*. The sentence should have been written like this:
● The hurricane ran *its* course.

We add the apostrophe to words when we shouldn't at other times, too:
● The *tree's* shook.
● The *house's* swayed.

Trees and *houses* are **plurals**. They do not need an apostrophe here.

A Fred had no time to proofread his article. He used 12 apostrophes where they are not needed. Write the piece out again, correcting his mistakes. REMEMBER: some apostrophes have been used correctly.

Cyclone Cyril

Freak weather has plagued the shores' along the USA's east coast for several weeks'. Some locals are battening down the hatches again, as meteorologists' track Cyclone Cyril's progress. Others' have left, seeking refuge in Florida's safer spots'. Cyclone Cyril will run it's course over the next few days'. The authorities' are hoping it will exhaust it'self as it comes in from the Atlantic. A spokesman, Hank Weatherby, commented: ''Cyril won't be as bad as Annie was in July, but we're taking no chances'. We're advising folks' to leave vulnerable areas' as soon as possible.''

Remember You need to check that you are using the *apostrophe* correctly.

Homophone Families

Homophones are words that sound the same, but have different spellings and different meanings. If you read these two words aloud, you will hear that they sound the same, but mean different things:

● *see   sea.*

When you are deciding which homophone to use, think of other words that have similar meanings. For example:

● *see, seeing, seen.*

A Each picture below contains members of two word families. Sort the words into two groups by putting together words with related meanings. For example: sailor, sailboard, sailing. Make lists of your words.

1. sale
sailor
wholesale
resale
sailboard
sailing

2. won
lone
winner
winning
win
only
once

3. son
sunburn
stepson
sunshine
sun
grandson
sunscreen

4. blew
blue
blow
bluebell
blowing
blown

5. eaten
eat
eighty
eighteen
ate
eight
eating

Remember You can remember *homophones* by matching them to their word families.

Homophone Connection

It is important to know which **homophone** is which so that you can use the right one when you write.

What do you call a gossipy dog?

A tail-bearer.

A Here are some homophone pairs. Write a sentence for each pair to show their meanings. For example: Where are you going to wear your new outfit?

1 wear / where

2 wood / would

3 tale / tail

4 weather / whether

5 pair / pear

6 piece / peace

7 past / passed

8 you're / your

9 hole / whole

10 in / inn

Remember Learning the meaning of *homophones* will help you to remember their spellings.

Noun Detective

A **noun** is a word that names a person, a place or a thing.

These nouns have a special name: **common nouns**. For example:

● *car   boat   door.*

Common nouns do not use capital letters unless the word begins a sentence.

A Write eight nouns that you might find in each of the following places:
1. space shuttle; 2. castle; 3. cave;
4. jungle.

Copy and Complete
1. space shuttle computer, astronaut ...

B Now choose one of these places and write a short story about an adventure you could have there. Underline all the common nouns that you use.

What has a horn
and drives?

A car.

Remember The name of a person, place or thing is called a *common noun.*

What's in a Name?

A **proper noun** is the name of a particular person, place or thing, such as *Cardiff*, *Hampshire* and the *Mary Rose*. Proper nouns are always written with capital letters at the beginning of the word. Many proper nouns are made up of two or more words, such as *City Hall*.

> What is a tornado?
>
> Mother Nature doing the twist.

A Read the words below. Then make two lists of proper and common nouns as shown in the 'Copy and Complete' chart. Remember to add a capital letter to the proper nouns.

Copy and Complete		
Common Nouns		
People	Places	Things
boys		

Copy and Complete		
Proper Nouns		
People	Places	Things
James		

james	park	baby	mother
computer	blanket	car	boys
snowdonia	castle	molly	office
manchester	street	carla	tower
aberdeen	water	father	ball
beach	venus	dentist	
japan	grand canyon		prime minister
tower of london		trafalgar square	

B Now add some more proper and common nouns to each list.

Remember A particular name of a person, place or thing is called a *proper noun*.

Geography Quiz

A Answer the following quiz. You may need to use an atlas to help you. What do you need to remember about writing **proper nouns** – the particular names of people, places or things?

1. The town where you live.

2. The name of your school.

3. Two cities in your country.

4. The capital of your country.

5. A river near where you live.

6. A street near your home.

7. Two oceans.

8. Two mountains.

9. A public building in your town.

10. A famous building in another country.

11. Two countries.

B Now develop four quiz questions of your own. Try them out on a classmate.

Remember A *proper noun* always starts with a capital letter.

Bigger and Better

An **adjective** can tell you how big or how small a person, place or thing is, or how many there are of them.

A Answer each of the questions below, including the italic adjectives in your answers. For example: What would you like to have *many* of? I would like *many* books to read because I enjoy reading.

1. What would you like to have *many* of?

2. What things are you too *short* to do?

3. What object would be impossible to use if it was *bigger*?

4. What do you think the world has too *few* of?

5. What do you think is too *narrow*?

6. What would be better if it were *smaller*?

7. What should always be as *wide* as possible?

B How many adjectives can you list that mean 'big' or 'small'?

Remember Some *adjectives* can describe size.

Alphabetical Verbs

Verbs are action words. They tell you what something or someone is doing.

A Look at the verbs in italics in this sentence. They begin with three consecutive letters of the alphabet: **b**, **c**, **d**.

Dilip *broke* a plate, *cracked* a glass and *dropped* his dinner on the floor.

● Write your own alphabetical verb sentences. Begin each verb with a different letter in alphabetical order. Use at least two verbs in each sentence.

Why did the elephant paint himself all different colours?

So that he could hide in a box of crayons.

Remember *Verbs* are words that describe action.

Change the Tense

A **verb** can tell you what is happening now, what happened in the past, or what will happen in the future. These are called **verb tenses**.

● **Present tense:**
I am *waiting* for the bus. Every day she *waits* for the bus.
● **Past tense:**
Yesterday, I *waited* for the bus.
● **Future tense:**
Tomorrow I *will wait* for the bus.

Add the endings **s**, **ed** or **ing** to change the verb tense. REMEMBER: with some words you need to change the final **y** to **i** or drop the final **e** before adding the ending.

A Look at the chart of words below. Write a sentence using these verbs in the correct tense. For example, the words *hurry* and *we* can be used in this way in the present tense: We hurry whenever we smell dinner.

Tense	Verb	Who
1. present	hurry	we
2. past	paste	he
3. future	stay	they
4. past	live	Mario
5. future	call	I
6. past	hope	she
7. present	wonder	I
8. past	cook	we
9. future	play	she
10. past	cry	they
11. present	smile	we

Why is a crossword puzzle like a quarrel?

Because one cross word leads to another.

Remember You can write *verbs* in the *past*, *present* and *future* tenses.

Scrambled Tenses

If something happened yesterday or in the past, we use **verbs** in the **past tense**. Most of the time, we write the past tense of the verb by adding **ed** to the end. For example:

● I walk   I *walked*
   I *have walked.*

Some verbs have **irregular past tenses**. For example:

● I know   I *knew*
   I *have known.*

A   Look at the past-tense verbs below. Can you unscramble them? After you have unscrambled the verbs, complete each sentence in your own words.

> **Copy and Complete**
>
> **1.** went I   have I gone
>   I went   I have gone
>
> I went home after school.
> I have gone shopping with my best friend.

Verbs	Scrambled	Past Tenses
1. I go	went I	have I gone
2. I take	took he	has he taken
3. I rise	rose they	risen they have
4. I give	gave she	she given has
5. I write	wrote I	I written have
6. I have	had he	had has he
7. I ring	rang it	rung it has
8. I speak	spoke they	they spoken have
9. I choose	chose I	have I chosen
10. I swim	swam she	swum she has
11. I do	did they	have they done
12. I wear	wore I	worn I have
13. I fly	flew it	it flown has
14. I come	came she	come has she

went
took rose
wrote gave
had rang spoke
chose swam did
wore flew came

Remember Some *verbs* have *irregular past tenses.*

45

Spice It Up!

Using interesting **verbs** can help to bring your writing to life and create interest for your reader.

What different pictures do these two sentences bring to mind?

- We *went* up the hill.
- We *scrambled* up the hill.

A Look at the sentences below. Think about more interesting verbs that could be used to replace the verbs in italics. Copy each sentence twice, each time using a different verb that means the same as the verb in italics. For example: The snow *swirled* to the ground.

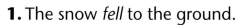

1. The snow *fell* to the ground.

2. The children *ran* down the hill.

3. Melanie *liked* the hamburger.

4. The wind *blew* outside my window.

5. Rain *hit* the roof.

6. Emma *jumped* into the water.

7. Fluffy *ate* her food.

8. I *called* across the street.

B Choose the most interesting new sentence. Write three sentences that might follow it in a story. Think about the verbs you use.

Remember Choose interesting *verbs* in your own writing.

Using Adverbs

We can use **adverbs** to emphasise **verbs**, but we have to use them carefully:

- Errol leapt *nimbly* on to his bike and rode away.
- Errol leapt *nimbly* on to his bike and rode *swiftly* away.

There are too many adverbs in the second sentence. We can guess that Errol will ride away *swiftly* because he *leapt nimbly* on to his bike, so we do not need to emphasise it.

If we use interesting verbs we often do not need to use adverbs. If we use ordinary verbs we could add adverbs:

- Errol *strolled* along.
- Errol *walked casually* along.

A Read the following passage and make a list of all the adverbs.

> Errol and Sally strolled towards the footpath. It was a bright day and they felt happy. On one side some sheep were lazily munching the grass and in the distance they could see the cloudless sky. Everything seemed perfect.
>
> They turned the corner at the edge of the field and suddenly Errol froze. Facing them and snorting loudly was a large bull with a ring in its nostrils. It worried the dusty path with one hoof and stared aggressively at the two children ...

B Now finish the second paragraph and write another to complete the story. Use adverbs such as *timidly* and *excitedly*. Look for words in a thesaurus.

- Read through your work. Does it flow well? Have you used too many adverbs?

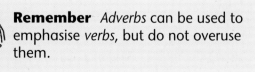

Remember *Adverbs* can be used to emphasise *verbs*, but do not overuse them.

The Numbers Game

You should remember that **pronouns** can replace **nouns** and **proper nouns**.

- Katie and Tim were ten years old. Katie and Tim lived in a large town.

It would be better to write:

- Katie and Tim were ten years old. *They* lived in a large town.

A Write out the following, replacing nouns and proper nouns with pronouns, where suitable. REMEMBER: you will sometimes need to keep nouns and proper nouns to make the meaning clear.

> Katie loved numbers. Katie had a calculator and played with the calculator for hours.
> "Ten fives are fifty, two elevens are twenty-two," Katie sang.
> Tim, Katie's twin brother, preferred basketball. Tim was an expert; Tim played for the school team. Basketball was Tim's main hobby.
> "How many balls have you netted this week?" Tim's sister asked Tim and together Tim and Katie totted up Tim's score.
>
> Now, Tim had a grand plan.
> Tim wanted to ...

B Finish the story. Try to use the pronouns: *I, we, you, me, us* and *them*.

We all have a *proper noun*. What's yours?

Remember You can use *pronouns* to replace *nouns* and *proper nouns*, but you should not overuse them.

The Cat Gets the Cream

Read the following. Decide which passage sounds strange.

a) The cat saunter into the kitchen and sniff the air. They smiles.

b) The cat saunters into the kitchen and sniffs the air. It smiles.

a) sounds strange because the **nouns**, **pronouns** and **verbs** do not agree.

Check a) again and see which words are different from those in b).

A The tale of the cat in the kitchen continues! Read the story, noting where the nouns, pronouns and verbs do not agree. You will see how the story is spoilt.

> The cat saunters into the kitchen and sniffs the air. It smiles. At the far corner stand the fridge. Their door is not quite shut. The cat turn its head and twitch its ears. Casually it rub its back against a cupboard. It cleans us tail. Nobody is watching. Nobody are listening. Before you can says "Cheshire Cat" a furry paw is inside the fridge! A tub of clotted cream tumble out and the contents spills onto the ground. The cat are delighted. It licks it lips and purrs a deep throaty purr, as it pushes its nose further into the tub.

● Write out the story, correcting it as you go. Then read the story again.

Which tense is the story written in?

Remember Your writing will not make sense if the *nouns, pronouns* and *verbs* do not agree.

Where Is It?

Have you heard the joke about the wall?

You'd never get over it!

A Here are 19 words that tell you where something might be. They are called **prepositions**.

● Use as many of these words as you can to describe features of your home. Underline each one as you go. For example: We have a painting of a lake <u>over</u> the fireplace.

over near into under

across

in on between behind

past from to

with

among at beside

above

below around

Remember *Prepositions* are words that can tell you where something is.

Mr Patel's Plan

We use **prepositions** to connect different parts of a sentence:

- Mr Patel, the town planner, put the model *on* his desk.

On is a preposition. It tells us where the model was put, or the position of it. Prepositions also help to make the meaning clear:

- Mr Patel, the town planner, put the model *in* his desk.

Changing the preposition can also change the meaning.

A Write out the passage about Mr Patel's Plan, putting the prepositions from the box in the most suitable places.

up	to	down	at
of	out	in	near	for

Mr Patel looked carefully _____ the model, rolled _____ his sleeves, took _____ his pen and wrote _____ some notes: 'sufficient space _____ the park, plenty _____ trees _____ the flats, buildings not too close _____ each other.' Then he paused _____ a moment and continued: 'Where's the adventure playground, the pond and the footpath?'

B Finish Mr Patel's notes, using the following prepositions:

along	around	into

Remember We use *prepositions* to link different parts of a sentence and to help to make the meaning clear.

51

Remember the Name

We use a **preposition** in front of the **noun** or **pronoun** to which it applies:

● I will share my sweets *with* him.

We also use certain prepositions with certain words:

● similar *to*
   different *from*.

Try to remember the name: **preposition**.

How many syllables in the word preposition?

A Draw a table like this:

Copy and Complete			
Noun	Verb	Adjective	Preposition

● Now put these words under the correct heading:

mouse	over	leap	dragon
quick	angel	cloudy	across
before	think	happy	chase
through	catch	beneath	good

B Look at the box below. Match the words to the most suitable preposition and write out your pairs. (You can use a preposition more than once, but you must use all of them.)

Words
according   pleased   suffer   rely
complain   cling   pass   share   expect
Prepositions
with   to   from   by   on   about

C Choose three pairs and use them to write sentences.

Remember We use a *preposition* in front of the *noun* or *pronoun* to which it belongs.

Another Word for Me

What do these words have in common?

- *huge   large   enormous   gigantic   massive.*

They are all words with almost the same meaning as *big*. Words that mean almost the same thing are called **synonyms.** When writing, you often have a choice of words to use. Choosing just the right word can make your writing more interesting.

A Look at the words being juggled below. Write at least four synonyms for each of these eight words. Make a list of your words.

said

ran

hungry

small

wet

tasty

clever

fell

B Revise a piece of your first-draft writing, concentrating on replacing common words with more interesting synonyms.

What is another name for a telephone booth?

A chatterbox.

Remember Words that have similar meanings are called *synonyms.*

Opposites Attract

Antonyms are words with opposite meanings. Sometimes you can create an antonym by adding a **prefix** to a word.

A Look at the words in the globe to create antonyms in different ways.

1. Build the antonyms of these words by adding a prefix. For example, the antonym of possible is **im**possible.

Prefixes					
dis	in	un	mis	im	ir

Words

a. ___possible **b.** ___honest **c.** ___appear **d.** ___active **e.** ___polite
f. ___responsible **g.** ___able **h.** ___known **i.** ___understand **j.** ___kind

2. You can also create antonyms by adding a **suffix**. Add the suffix **less** to these words to form antonyms.

a. care___   **b.** age___   **c.** pain___   **d.** home___   **e.** heart___

3. Some antonyms are different words. Write an antonym for each of the words below:

big in right bright good
wet high beautiful up wise
slow crooked long shiny

Remember Some *prefixes* change a word into its opposite. An opposite can be called an *antonym*.

Night and Day

REMEMBER: a **synonym** is a word which has a similar meaning to another. An **antonym** is a word which is opposite in meaning to another. For example:
● *day/night*
● *over/under*.

Some words have more than one antonym:
● *big/small, tiny.*

Other words can be changed into their opposite by adding or changing a **prefix** or a **suffix**:
● *important/**un**important*
● *thoughtful/thought**less***.

Sometimes we can use two or several words to make an opposite:
● *return/go away.*

A Write down one antonym for each word:

north	top	mother	quickly	go
there	mend	father-in-law		many

B Write down two antonyms for each of these words. Check in a thesaurus if you need to.

sad   truth   silence   near   calm

C Look at these words. Add, remove or change a suffix or prefix to make their antonyms:

comfortable   unselfish   cheerful   merciful
grateful   advantage   respectful

D Find two or several words that make an antonym of each of these:

together   behind   late

E Choose a pair of words (an antonym and a synonym) from your answers to each section above and write a sentence for each pair.

Remember An *antonym* is a word which is opposite in meaning to another.

55

Whoosh!

Using words that sound like their meanings is called **onomatopoeia** (on-o-mat-o-poei-a):

● *Crash! Scamper! Whoosh!*

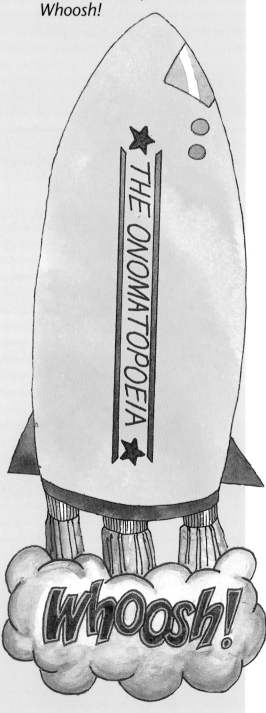

A Write down these four headings:

Copy and Complete			
light	heavy	sharp	wet

● Now write the following words under the heading that you think best describes the sound they make:

crick-crack   flip   grump   splash
flump   scuttle   whack   slip   snip
rustle   clomp   clip   skedaddle
drip   tinkle   waddle   slither

B Read the following poem:

Moving House

CLUMP THUMP
LUMP DUMP
CRASH SMASH
BISH BASH
BANG TWANG
FLIP TRIP
RING PING
TING-A-LING
JINGLE JONGLE JANGLE!

Mary Green

● Write your own poem about a rocket launch using onomatopoeia. You could describe the build-up to the launch and the rocket taking off.

 **Remember** Using words that sound like their meanings is called *onomatopoeia.*

Two Left Feet

We often use expressions to describe someone or a situation:

- Jane's got two left feet!

This does not mean that Jane really has got two left feet. It is a way of saying that she is clumsy.

We call this a **metaphor**. *Two left feet* stands in place of *clumsy*. Most expressions and figures of speech are metaphors.

A Match these figures of speech to their meanings. Write down the letters and numbers which match.

1. raining cats and dogs
2. make ends meet
3. nip in the bud
4. send packing
5. blow your own trumpet

a. stop something before it gets worse
b. boast
c. raining heavily
d. manage your money
e. dismiss someone

B Write down what each of these really means.

1. take the mickey
2. at a loose end
3. hard up
4. carried away
5. draw the line

C Draw a series of cartoons to show what *two left feet* really means.

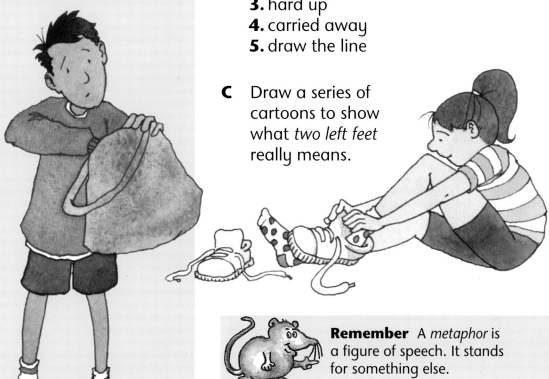

Remember A *metaphor* is a figure of speech. It stands for something else.

Words From Other Languages

Many societies today are multicultural and this is reflected in their languages. There are many everyday words that are part of English which come from other countries.

A Make four headings in your book:

Copy and Complete			
Spanish	Arabic	Hebrew	Italian

● Write down the following words under the language you think they come from:

spaghetti	patio	lemon	umbrella
vanilla	volcano	kosher	caravan
macaroni	jubilee	syrup	potato
cherub	algebra	banana	

● Check those that you do not know in a dictionary. Split the ones that you find difficult to spell into syllables. This will help you to remember them.

B Think of two everyday words that come from each of these places:
  a. India and Pakistan **b.** The Caribbean
  c. China

C Check the meaning of these harder words and find out where they come from. Write down two things that they have in common.
  a. soprano **b.** duet **c.** cello
  d. maestro **e.** libretto

● Split the words into their syllables.

Remember There are many ordinary English words which come from other countries.

The More the Merrier!

When we chat with our friends and people we know well, we often use sayings to express a feeling or describe a situation. A saying usually has a hidden meaning:

● "Can we use the Activities Room?" asked Alvin.
"Come in, *the more the merrier*!" replied the teacher.

The saying really means that the teacher *is happy to include everyone.*

A Match these sayings to their real meanings:

Copy and Complete
1. = C.

1. under the weather	**A.** avoid getting to the point
2. past his prime	**B.** too much, exaggerated
3. given up the ghost	**C.** feeling unwell
4. taken for a ride	**D.** pretend nothing is wrong
5. not up to it	**E.** upsetting someone
6. put on a brave face	**F.** given up trying
7. over the top	**G.** deceived
8. beat about the bush	**H.** not capable of doing something
9. in for a penny, in for a pound	**I.** average chance, suitable
10. par for the course	**J.** will take a risk
11. putting his back up	**K.** past his best

B Now choose five of the above sayings and write a question and answer for each, as shown in the example in the left-hand column.

Remember Common sayings often have hidden meanings.

Check It Out!

Did you know that dictionaries have other information besides the meaning and spelling of words?

This information is kept in the **appendix** or **reference section**.

A Look up the word *appendix* in your dictionary. Write down what it means.

B What is in your dictionary appendix? Write down which, if any, of these are in the appendix:

1. Prefixes and suffixes
2. Months of the year
3. Calendar
4. Planets of the solar system
5. Days of the week
6. Countries of the world
7. Weights and measures
8. Abbreviations

C What else is in the appendix? Write it down.

D Now write down two facts from each section along with the appendix or page number.

E Using your dictionary appendix or another reference book find out the answers to the following:

1. What is a Great Dane?
2. Where would you spend yen?
3. What belongs to a gaggle?
4. Where does a Saudi come from?

What month is a soldier?

March.

Remember A dictionary usually has an *appendix* or *reference section*.

Set Some Questions

You will need to use the **appendix** in your dictionary or a reference book.

A Which information interests you most in the appendix – the planets, the calendar, abbreviations?

● You are going to make a question sheet. Choose two sections in the appendix and five questions about each one for a friend to answer. For example, here are five questions about the planets:

1. Who was Mercurius?
2. What does the name Earth mean?
3. What is the Greek name for Pluto?
4. Who was the most ancient of the Greek gods?
5. Who was the Roman god of the sea?

● Write a heading for your question sheet. Your friend must write down the appendix and/or the page number, so write instructions about this.

Time how long your friend takes to find the answers.

B Now try to find the answers to the questions in section A.

What notes do the planets sing?

Solar!

Remember A dictionary usually has a *reference section* or an *appendix*.

Word Detective

To find words in a dictionary, thesaurus or other reference material, you need to know **alphabetical order.**

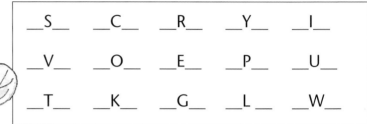

What is the biggest building?

The library. It has the most stories.

A Copy the letters in the box below. Write the letters that come before and after them.

_S_	_C_	_R_	_Y_	_I_
_V_	_O_	_E_	_P_	_U_
_T_	_K_	_G_	_L_	_W_

B Put the words in the books below into alphabetical order. When words begin with the same letter, use the second letter and so on in the words to help you.

1
apple
bottle
arch
apart
boot

2
moving
mountain
move
mist
myth

3
zap
zesty
zip
zoo
zoology

4
stream
steam
street
repeat
report

Remember To find words in a dictionary or thesaurus, you need to know *alphabetical order.*

It's Your Guide

There are two **guide words** at the top of each dictionary page. The guide word on the left shows you what the first word on the page is. The guide word on the right shows you what the last word is.

A In each list below, the guide words are highlighted. Copy each list, carefully keeping the words in the same order. On your list, underline all the words that come between the two guide words.

Copy and Complete

1. **bleak** <u>blend</u> <u>blink</u> blade blaze <u>blizzard</u> **block**

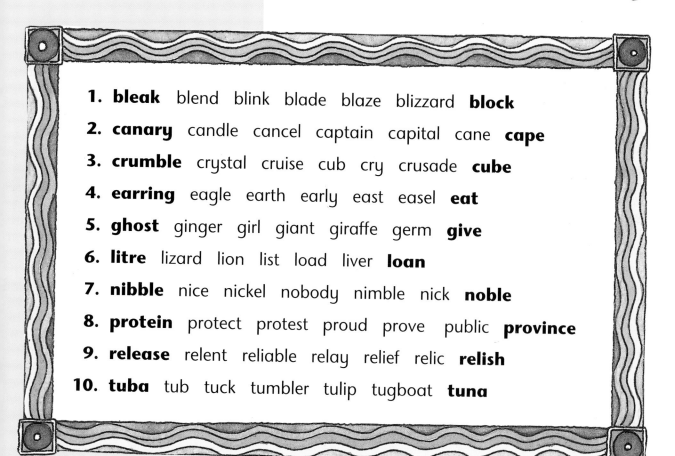

1. **bleak** blend blink blade blaze blizzard **block**
2. **canary** candle cancel captain capital cane **cape**
3. **crumble** crystal cruise cub cry crusade **cube**
4. **earring** eagle earth early east easel **eat**
5. **ghost** ginger girl giant giraffe germ **give**
6. **litre** lizard lion list load liver **loan**
7. **nibble** nice nickel nobody nimble nick **noble**
8. **protein** protect protest proud prove public **province**
9. **release** relent reliable relay relief relic **relish**
10. **tuba** tub tuck tumbler tulip tugboat **tuna**

Remember *Guide words* help you to find words in a dictionary.

Mixed-Up Recipes

A **table of contents** lists the contents of a book and organises them under headings so that you can find the information you need.

A Write a table of contents for a cookbook using the recipe titles listed below. Sort the recipes using these chapter headings: *Meat Dishes, Pastas and Grains, Vegetable Dishes* and *Delicious Desserts*.

Strawberry Mousse

Greek Salad

Spicy Meatballs

Barbecued Ribs

Chilli

Chocolate Cheesecake

Courgette Pancakes

Carrot Cake

Bhindi Bhaji

Lemon Meringue

Roast Lamb

Mixed-Vegetable Stir Fry

Upside-Down Cake

Blackcurrant Pancakes

Macaroni Cheese

Vegetable Biryani

Risotto

Spaghetti Bolognese

Remember A *table of contents* tells you what is in a book and where to find it.

What Do We Say?

We all use **dialects** (speak English in different ways), depending on where we live. There is nothing wrong with this. Writers often give their characters dialects to make them seem true to life:

- **Sandy:**
  We seen you and Kitty yesterday. Where was you going?
  Sue:
  We was going home.

We can also use standard English. This is like a dialect which is used in most kinds of writing. When we use standard English the **verbs**, **nouns**, **pronouns** and **tenses** need to agree:

- **Sandy:**
  We saw you and Kitty yesterday. Where were you going?
  Sue:
  We were going home.

A Write these sentences in standard English so that the verb agrees with the noun:

1. I seen the film last week.
2. I goes to my grandmother's every Friday.
3. Our kittens loves playing with the string.
4. We comes home at six o'clock.
5. Them two is always playing football.

B Write a letter to a friend telling them about a holiday in which the tourist company forgot to book your hotel. You can use non-standard dialect if you wish.

C Now write a letter to the tourist company in standard English complaining about their mistake.

Where were you going?

We were going home.

Remember Standard English is like a *dialect* that is used in most kinds of writing.

Oh, No!

Some sentences express strong feelings. These are called **exclamations** and end with an **exclamation mark**:

- Oh no, not that again**!**
- Quick, the milk is boiling over**!**

Some sentences ask a **question** and end with a **question mark**:

- Did you leave the computer on**?**

A What do you think the people in the park scene below are saying? Make a list of your answers.

What did the paper say to the pencil?

Write on!

Remember An *exclamation mark* is used to express strong feelings. We sometimes use them when we are writing conversation or dialogue.

What a Day!

Look again at the picture on page 66. The picture uses **speech bubbles** to let you know what people are saying. In a story, writers use **speech marks** (" ") to show when someone is talking.

A Choose one of the characters from the scene and write an account of his or her day. Include dialogue between the characters.

What is a baby computer's first word?

"Da-ta."

Remember Use *speech marks* when you write dialogue.

List Them

The **colon** is a pause that can be used to give instructions or list information like this:

● Mr Marvel played five instruments**:** the tuba, the bassoon, the trumpet, the trombone and the saxophone.

You will see that **commas** are used to separate the items.

A Write out these sentences, putting in the colon and the commas in the correct places:

1. Naomi was visiting three countries Holland Belgium and France.
2. She had already packed several items for the trip a toothbrush some toothpaste and a towel.
3. The day before she travelled she had to collect a few things some traveller's cheques a new passport and her ticket.
4. She also bought presents for her relations in Holland which she packed a pair of gloves a pair of yellow bloomers a pair of socks and some booties for the baby.

B Naomi forgot to pack some items. Look carefully at the picture below to see what she forgot. Write a sentence listing what they are.

Remember A *colon* can be used in a list of items.

How to Measure an Elephant

We can use **commas** to separate different parts of a sentence. Read this sentence – it has no commas:

● Kris and Surjit who were classmates lived next door to each other.

Now read it again. Change the expression of your voice when you read the part that is surrounded by commas.

● Kris and Surjit, who were classmates, lived next door to each other.

The phrase *who were classmates* gives us extra information about Kris and Surjit and we can separate this from the rest of the sentence with commas.

A Write down these sentences putting *one* or *two* commas in the correct places:

1. Kris and Surjit had been asked to measure an elephant which came from the nearby zoo as part of a school project.
2. Their friend Millie said that she would help them.
3. The elephant whose name was Bessie was a very docile creature.
4. Carrying the tape measure Kris and Surjit climbed onto Bessie's back.
5. With some difficulty they took Bessie's measurements.
6. Millie using a paper and pencil wrote down the figures.

B Look carefully at the picture and write three more sentences about it, using commas.

Remember We can use *commas* to separate parts of a sentence.

Jake's Life

As you know, we can use **commas** to separate parts of a sentence. Read the following:

- Jake, *who was ten years old*, was to star in his own show.

Who was ten years old is extra information about Jake. It can be written with commas surrounding it.

We can also use **colons** in sentences when we want to write a **list**:

- Jake had several talents**:** painting, model-making and film-making.

REMEMBER: commas are also used when you write a list.

A Jake had won the Young Film Maker of the Year competition three years in a row and his local television company decided to tell his life story. Here is some of the information they collected about him. Write it out, putting commas or colons in the correct places.

1. Jake who had many relatives was a happy boy.
2. Jake's family including his younger sister all made films.
3. Good ideas as well as model-making skills helped Jake to make interesting films.
4. Jake had many pets a cat a dog a snake four rabbits and a pair of geese.
5. The family pets had appeared in the following films *Free Whiskers A Dog's Life The Hissstory of Snakes Four Rabbits in Search of a Hutch* and *Wild Geese over Wimbledon*.
6. *Jake's Life* which was to be seen by millions would be Jake's first appearance on television.

Remember You may need to use punctuation marks in complex sentences.

"Who's There?"

● Knock, knock!
"Who's there?"
"Willie."
"Willie who?"
"Will he never open the door?"

You may remember that the words in **speech marks** are the actual words spoken. We call this **direct speech**.

The joke above partly depends on using direct speech. Listen to how it sounds if we use **reported speech**. (We use this kind of speech when we report what has happened. It is in the **past tense**.)

● There was a knock at the door. He asked who was there and the reply came that it was Willie.

Try finishing this. You will find that the joke is completely lost!

A You can change some conversations into reported speech. You will need to change the order of words, add new ones, write in the past tense and drop the speech marks. Choose the conversation that can be *easily changed* and write it in reported speech.

1. "Whack!" Karl shouted as he threw the ball against the door.
"Ouch!" replied Sam, entering the room.
2. "Are you going to the party?" asked Sue.
"I'll let you know tomorrow," replied Sonia.

B Change the following from reported speech to direct speech:

Frankie explained that she had bought the new trainers yesterday but when she tried them on they pinched her feet. Ben told her to return them to the shop, adding that she could probably get her money back.

Remember You cannot easily change some speech from *direct* to *reported*.

Add a Word

What is missing in this sentence?

● Ran all the way.

It needs a **noun** so that you know *who* ran.

What is missing in the next sentence?

● Everyone on the team.

It needs a **verb** so that you know *what* everyone did.

A sentence needs both a noun and a verb to make it complete.

A The following sentences contain only two words, a noun and a verb. Rewrite each sentence several times, adding only one word each time. How long can you make each sentence?

> ## Copy and Complete
>
> **1.** Bears eat.
> **Brown** bears eat.
> Brown bears eat **honey**.
> Brown bears **always** eat honey.
> **Wild** brown bears always eat honey.

1. Bears eat.
2. Flowers bloom.
3. Snow falls.
4. Children play.
5. Wheels turn.

B Now write a two-word sentence of your own then write several sentences, adding one word each time.

Remember Sentences need both a *noun* and *verb* to make them complete.

Two Parts

All sentences begin with a capital letter and end with a punctuation mark. Most sentences have two parts. One part (the **subject**) tells you who or what the sentence is about. The other part (the **predicate**) tells you what is happening.

A Copy the sentences below. Underline each subject and circle each predicate in them.

   1. Birds fly.   **2.** Fish swim.   **3.** Children play.

B Copy the sentences below and complete them by filling in the subject.

   1. _____ are going to the park.
   2. _____ ran to catch the bus.
   3. _____ blasted off into the sky.

C Copy the sentences below and complete them by writing what you think is happening (the predicate).

   1. Fire _____ .
   2. Cats _____ .
   3. My friends _____ .

D Now write four sentences explaining what is happening in each of these pictures. Underline the subject and circle the predicate in each of your sentences.

Remember The *subject* of a sentence tells you who or what the sentence is about and the *predicate* tells you what is happening.

Phrase It Right

A **phrase** is a group of words that expresses an idea, but is not a complete sentence on its own.

A Look at some phrases in the box below. They might be used to describe something.

> with the long tail   from the shop window
> in the scuffed running shoes
> on the path   beside my bed

● Copy the sentences below and complete them using the phrases in the box.

1. I dropped my slippers on the rug
_____ .

2. Jamal had to climb over the bicycle
_____ .

3. Is that the stuffed toy _____ ?

4. The mouse _____ looked out curiously from under the table.

5. The girl _____ won the race easily.

B Copy the sentences below and add a phrase to each of them. Start each phrase with one of the words in the box. For example: 1. The kangaroo with the flippers and snorkel was the most interesting animal I ever saw.

> with   from   in   of   on   that

1. The kangaroo _____ was the most interesting animal I ever saw.

2. A bag _____ was left on the bus.

3. The dragon _____ emerged from the forest.

4. The clown _____ rode a unicycle around the ring.

Remember A *phrase* is a group of words with no verb. It is part of a sentence.

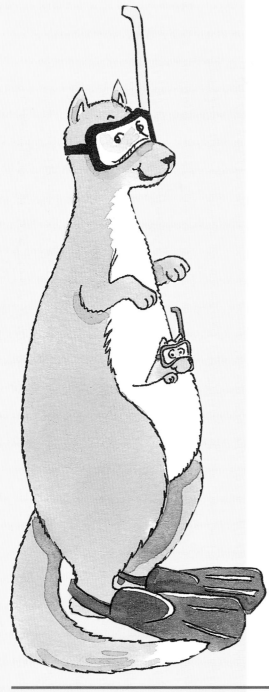

74

What's It All About?

A **phrase** is a group of words that expresses an idea. It can tell you *when, where, why* or *how* something happened.

A The phrases in the sentences below are highlighted. Look at the words in the box and use them to describe each phrase. Does the phrase tell you when, where, why or how something happened?

when	where	why	how

1. The wolves **in the woods** howled all night.
2. I was late getting home **because of the snowstorm**.
3. **With a final effort**, the horse crossed the finish line.
4. We will leave **right after breakfast**.

B Look at the phrases in the box below. Write eight new sentences using them. Say whether each sentence fits under the category of *when, where, why* or *how*. For example: I have been learning the violin since school started. (when)

since school started	after the storm
in a nervous voice	under the rug
outside the back door	every weekend
because of my brother	with a great roar

Remember A *phrase* can tell you when, where, why or how something happened.

Misplaced Phrases

What is wrong with this sentence?

● For sale, piano, by gentleman with beautifully carved legs.

The **phrase** has been misplaced and the sentence no longer says what the writer intended.

A Look at the sentences below, in which the phrases have been misplaced. Rewrite them so that they say what the writer really means.

> **Copy and Complete**
>
> 1. Donna passed a new computer store riding her bike.
>   Riding her bike, Donna passed a new computer store.

1. Donna passed a new computer store riding her bike.
2. Falling from the trees I saw apples.
3. An orange girl's jacket was left on the bus.
4. André saw his father's car swimming across the canal.
5. We saw the three-masted schooner on the way to lunch.
6. Paige waited for the bus with a smile.
7. The dog snapped at the postman baring his teeth in a snarl.
8. Mario saw a chicken roller-blading down the street.
9. The lumberjack climbed the tree wearing boots and thick socks.
10. I photographed a moose wearing my pyjamas.

You will need to add a comma to some of these sentences.

Remember Make sure you put your *phrases* in the right place!

Build a Sentence

Sentences have common parts such as **nouns**, **verbs**, **adjectives**, **adverbs** and **phrases**. They help to add details and to create interest for the reader.

A Copy the columns below and fill in the spaces to create your own sentences.

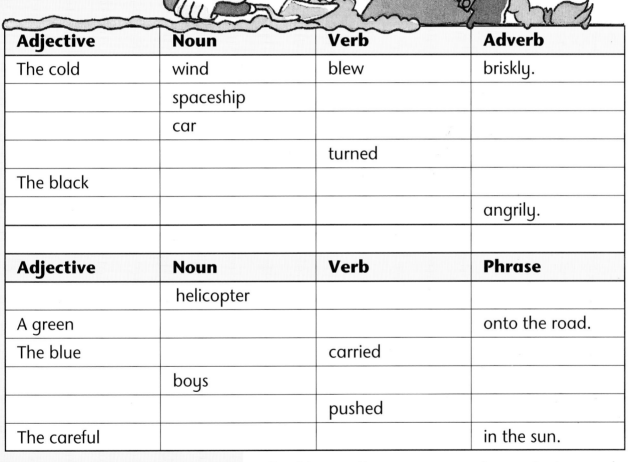

Adjective	Noun	Verb	Adverb
The cold	wind	blew	briskly.
	spaceship		
	car		
		turned	
The black			
			angrily.

Adjective	Noun	Verb	Phrase
	helicopter		
A green			onto the road.
The blue		carried	
	boys		
		pushed	
The careful			in the sun.

B Now write your own sentence starters and challenge someone in your class to finish them.

Remember You can build a sentence using *nouns*, *verbs*, *adjectives*, *adverbs* and *phrases*.

Raymond's Recipe

Another name for a simple sentence is a **clause**.

● Raymond made a trifle.

A longer sentence will have extra information. This is not as important as the **main clause** and is not a sentence on its own:

● Raymond made a trifle *for the family when he had time.*

Read the part in italics and you will see that it does not make sense on its own.

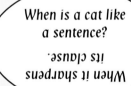

When is a cat like a sentence?

When it sharpens its clause.

A Write out the main clause in these sentences:

1. Raymond bought some fruit for the trifle yesterday at the greengrocer's.
2. He prepared the ingredients after he returned home from school.
3. He made the sponge, which was very light, using flour, sugar and fresh eggs.
4. Before making the jelly and custard, he chopped up the apples, pears, bananas and oranges.
5. The cream was added to the trifle as a final touch.
6. Bonzo waited patiently at the kitchen door for scraps.

custard   pears   sugar
flour   eggs
bananas
apples
jelly   milk
cream   oranges

Remember A *main clause* is a simple sentence.

Too Much Ketchup!

We can connect **clauses** to make longer sentences. For example:

- Ricky loved chips. He only loved crispy chips. He loved plenty of ketchup.

It sounds better if we say:

- Ricky loved chips *if* they were crispy *with* plenty of ketchup.

If and *with* are **connecting words**. We can also use **connecting phrases**:

- Tiffany was Ricky's sister. Tiffany also loved crispy chips. She loved plenty of ketchup.

It flows better if we say:

- Tiffany, *who was Ricky's sister*, also loved crispy chips with plenty of ketchup.

Finally, we can combine the two main sentences to make one:

- Ricky and his sister Tiffany loved chips if they were crispy with plenty of ketchup.

A Combine these groups of sentences into one. Use connecting words and phrases.

1. Ricky was hungry. He had not eaten much that day.
2. He cooked some chips. They were not very crispy.
3. He cooked a hamburger. It was not very juicy.
4. The meal was unappetising. The chips were cold. The hamburger did not sizzle on the plate.
5. Ricky grabbed the ketchup. He banged the end of the bottle. The ketchup shot out. It covered everything!

B Now combine the sentences you have made into a paragraph.

Remember You can use *connecting words* to link sentences.

Getting Organised

A sentence will have a **main clause**. It may also have extra information called a **subordinate clause**:

- Jackie was given a calendar *which she hung up*.

This type of clause is not as important as the main clause and does not make a sentence on its own. (Read the words in italics to check.)

A Jackie wrote some important messages on her calendar. Copy the sentences below, underlining the main clause in red and the subordinate clause in black.

1. Mum will collect my bracelet which is being mended.
2. I must pick up the tickets that Gran bought for us.
3. Molly will arrive after she has visited Keith.

B Now finish these sentences by thinking of main clauses. Write them down.

1. _____ which will cost £25.
2. Before they forget _____ .
3. _____ if you are too late.
4. _____ because she could not go.
5. After he has sent the card _____ .
6. _____ who is always late.
7. When her birthday party is finished _____ .

Remember A *subordinate clause* is not a sentence on its own.

The Main Action

REMEMBER: a **clause** is a sentence with a **subject** and a **verb**. For example: Lions roar.

A The following clauses all make sense by themselves. They tell you the main thing that is happening. They are called **main clauses**. Add two main clauses of your own to the list.

> I live on Elm Street.
> You can come to my party.
> It started to rain.
> You can watch the game on television.
> I missed the beginning of the concert.

B The following **subordinate clauses** do not make sense alone. They add detail to a sentence, but they need a main clause to tell what is happening. Add two subordinate clauses of your own to the list.

> because the bus was late
> if you get home in time
> after the rehearsal
> next to the bicycle shop
> while we were having dinner

C Build new sentences by combining the main clauses above with the subordinate clauses. You may use each part only once. You can start with either part. For example: After the rehearsal you can come to my party.

Remember A *clause* is a sentence with a subject and a verb. The *main clause* tells you the main thing that is happening.

Which Way?

We can write sentences in different ways and still keep the main point:

- *Scruff, Josie's dog*, liked to play with a tennis ball in the garden.
- *Josie's dog, Scruff*, liked to play in the garden with a tennis ball.

We could also remove some words and still keep the main point:

- Scruff liked to play with a ball in the garden.
- Josie's dog liked to play in the garden with a ball.

A Write each of these sentences in a different way:

1. After eating his favourite food Scruff played with his new ball on the lawn.
2. He escaped through a small hole in the fence at the bottom of the garden.
3. The young terrier, though he was in a nearby field, could not find his way back.
4. Josie's friend, Séamus, saw Scruff and after calling to him, took him straight home.
5. Josie gave silly old Scruff a big cuddle and thanked Séamus warmly.

B Now look through the sentences and write them again, removing any words you can without changing the meaning.

You can remove words such as adjectives and adverbs and keep the meaning of your sentence.

Remember We can write a sentence in a different way without changing the meaning.

82

Mix and Match

As you know, we can construct sentences in different ways and still keep the meaning. For example, we can take out some words:

- The *tiny boat* disappeared from view as we reached the shore.
- The boat disappeared from view as we reached the shore.

Or we can replace the words:

- The *small vessel* disappeared from view as we reached the *coast*.

A Write each sentence again in two ways. In the first sentence, you should leave out an **adjective**. In the second sentence, you should replace an **adjective**, **noun** and **verb** with ones of similar meaning.

1. Rachel clutched her red jacket and ran out of the room.
2. The grey clouds billowed across the darkening sky.
3. The beautiful mare trotted over to the railings, her foal behind her.
4. Jack was surprised by a deafening roar and he turned around.
5. The fierce animal blocked her way and she did not know what to do.
6. A good-humoured crowd had assembled at the corner of the street.

How could a thesaurus help you with this page?

Remember We can leave out words or replace them with similar ones and keep the meaning of a sentence.

Have a Go!

We use verbs in a special way when we give orders or draw attention to something. For example:

● "Now, look carefully!" exclaimed the teacher to her class.

The teacher is really saying, "Now, you look carefully!" We call this the **imperative**.

● "Who is looking carefully?" asked the teacher.

When we use words such as *who, whose, which, what* to ask questions, we call this the **interrogative**.

A Read the following conversation and write down the imperatives and interrogatives.

Fairfield School was having its Summer Fête and Jamie and Kisha were making plans. They had been given the responsibility of running the Lucky Dip.
"What's left to do?" asked Jamie.
"We need to find a place for the stall and advertise it."
"Okay, I'll make a poster," continued Jamie. "What shall I write? Which colours shall I use? Where shall I put it?"
"First things first! Let's find a place," exclaimed Kisha. "Look! That's a good spot." She was looking at a patch of grass near the entrance. "Come on! Be quick!" But Jamie was staring into the distance ...

B Finish the story, including some imperatives and interrogatives of your own.

Remember When you give an order you use the *imperative*. When you ask a question using **wh** words, you use the *interrogative*.

A Noise in the Night

Read the following:

- *Tommy* bought a new torch.

This type of sentence is called the **active** because it puts *Tommy*, or the **subject**, first.

- *A new torch* was bought by Tommy.

This type of sentence is called the **passive** because we put what has been bought (*a new torch*), or the **object**, first.

A Two of these sentences are passive. Decide which ones and write them down. Then change them into active sentences.

1. Tommy made a chocolate cake.
2. He put cream and jam in the middle.
3. He decorated it with tiny sweets.
4. Lindy, Tommy's sister, ate the largest slice.
5. Some was eaten by Tommy's mum and dad.
6. Tommy gave Biff the cat a piece.
7. He also gave Beauty the budgie a few crumbs.
8. The rest was finished by Rex the dog.

B Now read the following:

1. Suddenly, a noise startled Tommy.
2. He kept his new torch on his bedside table.

- Write six more active sentences of your own. Use the characters and ideas on the page to help you.

Check the meaning of the words *active* and *passive* in the dictionary to help you to understand.

Remember In an *active* sentence we place the *subject* of the sentence at the beginning.

At the Bottom of the Well

If you are writing a story for your friend or teacher to read, your sentences and words can be complicated. If you are writing a story for a young child to read, your sentences and words need to be simpler. So, you can write in different ways according to your **audience**. For example:

● Once, long ago, in a distant land, where the mountain ranges touched the sky and the oceans plumbed the depths ...

To make it simpler we might write:

● Once upon a time there was a faraway land. The mountains were high. The seas were deep.

A Now read the beginning of this story and rewrite it to make it simpler:

Once, long ago, at the bottom of a stagnant well, so deep that nobody could see the bottom, there lived an ancient toad. He was a gloomy creature, just as you would be if you had not seen the light for centuries. Each day slipped into another and each was the same as the next, so that the ancient toad began to forget what time it was. How little he imagined his life was about to change!

B Finish the story using simple sentences and words and give your story a title. Add drawings and make your story into a book for small children to read.

 **Remember** You should make your sentences difficult or simple according to your *audience*.

Be a Proofreader

Good writers must also be **proofreaders**. You will need to check your writing carefully to make sure that there are no errors in spelling, sentences or punctuation.

A Read the story below, then follow the instructions on the next page to help you to proofread the story.

The Loyal Sultan

Their once live a sultan. His name was Sultan Jamal and he is ruler of the land of persea. Sultan jamal spends long hours at work helping people with their problem such as shortage of food and water. Sultan Jamal know what it was like to be pour. He was once a pour man until he save Sultan Hassan life. It all started one day when Sultan Hassan was walking threw the market place on a tour of the city. Sudenly, a loud roar is heard. Evryone look around in fear but could not see any thing. Out of nowhere it seemed a large dragon droped out of the sky and landed in front of Sultan Hassan. The townspeople ran in terror, but Sultan Hassan stood him ground and face the dragon. This was not a good idea because the dragon could breath a deadly flame. He opend his mouth and began to breathe fire onto the Sultan.

Jamal had invented a new contraption that took water from the well threw what he called a hose. He was outside his humble shop watering the herb garden with the hose when he say the dragon about to burn the Sultan with the deadly flame. Not thinking about his own safety, he turned the hose onto the dragon. Startled be the sudden feeling of cold water in it's face the dragon flew away.

Sultan Hassan thanked Jamal for his help.

"You've saved my life. Since I have no children or other family, you shall inherit my title after my death. I know I can trust you to look after this land after I'm gone." Many years later Jamal became the new Sultan of Persea, and as Sultan Hassan had predicted, he took good care of the sultanate.

Remember *Proofreading* will help you to notice mistakes.

Be a Proofreader (continued)

Follow these steps to **proofread** the story about Sultan Jamal. Make sure that you follow each step carefully.

A Copy the story *exactly* as it appears on page 87, then correct it, following the instructions below. Leave a space between each line of text.

Copy and Complete

Their~~ ~~once live, a sultan ...   There/   d/

---

1. Read the story again, and make sure there is a **capital letter** at the beginning and a **full stop** at the end of every sentence.
2. Find all the **proper names** of people, places and things, and make sure they start with capital letters.
3. Find any **homophones** – words that sound the same but can be spelled in two ways and have different meanings. Make sure the spelling of each is correct.
4. Look for any **contractions** or **possessive words** that are missing an **apostrophe**.
5. Read the story again, and put in any missing **commas**.
6. Check one last time, and correct any spelling errors you find.

B Now write or type a final draft of the story on another piece of paper, correcting all the errors you found.
- Ask someone to check your rewritten version.
- The next time you proofread your writing, check through it more than once. Look for a different kind of error each time, as you did here.

Remember *Proofreading* will help you to notice mistakes.